STEVENSON • ELLIS • WATTERS • ALLEN

LUMBERJANES™

BEWARE THE KITTEN HOLY

BOOM!
BOX™

BOOM! BOX™

LUMBERJANES Volume One Scholastic Edition, June 2015. Published by BOOM! Box, a division of Boom Entertainment, Inc. Lumberjanes is ™ & © 2015 Boom Entertainment, Inc. Originally published in single magazine form as LUMBERJANES No. 1-4. ™ & © 2014 Boom Entertainment, Inc. All rights reserved. BOOM! Box™ and the BOOM! Box logo are trademarks of Boom Entertainment, Inc., registered in various countries and categories. All characters, events, and institutions depicted herein are fictional. Any similarity between any of the names, characters, persons, events, and/or institutions in this publication to actual names, characters, and persons, whether living or dead, events, and/or institutions is unintended and purely coincidental. BOOM! Box does not read or accept unsolicited submissions of ideas, stories, or artwork.

For information regarding the CPSIA on this printed material, call: (203) 595-3636 and provide reference RICH# – 619194. A catalog record of this book is available from OCLC and from the BOOM! Studios website, www.boom-studios.com, on the Librarians Page.

BOOM! Studios, 5670 Wilshire Boulevard, Suite 450, Los Angeles, CA 90036-5679. Printed in USA. First Printing.

ISBN: 978-1-60886-783-7, eISBN: 978-1-61398-454-3

THIS LUMBERJANES FIELD MANUAL BELONGS TO:

NAME:_____

TROOP:_____

DATE INVESTED:_____

FIELD MANUAL TABLE OF CONTENTS

LUMBERJANES
FIELD MANUAL

For the Intermediate Program

Tenth Edition • January 1984

Prepared for the
**Miss Qiunzella Thiskwin
Penniquiqul Thistle Crumpet's**
CAMP FOR ~~GIRLS~~ HARDCORE LADY-TYPES

"Friendship to the Max!"

A MESSAGE FROM THE LUMBERJANES HIGH COUNCIL

As young women, we were wild with the love of what the world had to offer—the trees, the birds, the wood-herbs and the live things that left their nightly tracks in the mud around our windows. We wanted to learn about them, to know the name of this or that wonderful bird, or brilliant flower. There were other things in the green and living world that had a binding charm for us, the almost unnatural call of curiosity to see what the world held. We wanted to learn to camp out, to live not only like the lady we were already growing up to be but to also learn tricks of winning comfort from the relentless wilderness.

It was then that we became Lumberjanes scouts, learning the joy of cutting wood with an axe, about the stars, the birds, the quadrupeds, the fish, the insects, the plants, telling their names; their hidden power or curious ways, about the camper's life the language of signs and even some of the secrets of the trail. It was at a Lumberjanes camp that we found our life's calling and the power of the tradition of helping young girls grow into the powerful ladies that they are.

Whether you are a dancer or a misfit, a career girl or the social elite, you have a place at this camp—no matter how different you feel. Being a Lumberjane is more than a short chapter in the continually growing pages of your life; it will show you the mysteries of life and the mysteries about yourself while still teaching you as much about the outdoor world that you wish to know. This handbook is meant to guide you on your path as a Lumberjane, as a friend, and as a human being. We hope it will show you a different side of life that will help guide you on your future journeys.

THE LUMBERJANES PLEDGE

I solemnly swear to do my best
Every day, and in all that I do,
To be brave and strong,
To be truthful and compassionate,
To be interesting and interested,
To pay attention and question
The world around me,
To think of others first,
To always help and protect my friends,

~~To apologize to yourself and faith in God,~~

And to make the world a better place
For Lumberjane scouts
And for everyone else.

THEN THERE'S A LINE ABOUT GOD, OR WHATEVER

LUMBERJANES ™

BEWARE THE KITTEN HOLY

Written by
Noelle Stevenson & Grace Ellis

Illustrated by
Brooke Allen

Colors by
Maarta Laiho

Letters by
Aubrey Aiese

Character Designs.....**Noelle Stevenson & Brooke Allen**
Badge Designs..**Kate Leth**
Lumberjanes Logo Design............**Hannah Nance Partlow**
Designer..**Scott Newman**
Assistant Editor.......................................**Whitney Leopard**
Editor...**Dafna Pleban**
*Special thanks to **Kelsey Pate** for giving the Lumberjanes their name.*

Created by Shannon Watters, Grace Ellis & Noelle Stevenson

LUMBERJANES FIELD MANUAL
CHAPTER ONE

Lumberjanes "Out-of-Doors" Program Field

UP ALL NIGHT BADGE

"Learn what goes bump in the night."

While nature is a great experience in the light of the sun, when majority of the living creatures are out and about, a true Lumberjane knows that there is even more to experience when the sun goes down. Curiosity and courage are especially important to a Lumberjane, she has an urge to get out and match her wits and fervor with the elements, to feel the cool crisp night air or possibly the rain in her face. To witness the hyper-natural power of lightning with the true darkness that a night with no moon can provide.

A Lumberjane knows about the experience and possible truths that can be found when the rest of the world is asleep. It is the urge to learn how to lay and follow trails, identify the healing abilities of the local fauna, how to walk great distances and run even farther, and how to work around the unnatural and supernatural forces that a Lumberjane is bound to confront. The *Up*

All Night badge is the for Lumberjane that has already conquered the unknown in the daylight and is ready to explore the adventure of the night, ready to discover how to use all the ways of getting from one place to another. A Lumberjane is able to enjoy all of the known and unknown things that can be found in their world.

To obtain the *Up All Night* badge a Lumberjane must have enjoyed the sunset on a cool crisp afternoon with a group of cherished friends. She must have walked under the canvas of the stars and enjoyed their beauty while going where her curiosity takes her. She must have enjoyed the first wind of a new day with the moon above her head and without sleep, energetically explored the new possibility of viewing the world under a moon. And her final step to obtaining this particular badge, is she would have had to enjoy the sunset of the new day surrounded by her friends and ready to start

I solemnly swear to do my best
Every day, And in all that I do,
To be brave and strong,
To be truthful and compassionate,
To be interesting and interested,
To respect nature,
To pay attention and question
The world around me,
To think of others first,
To *always* help and protect my friends
Then there's a line about god or whatever
And to make the world a better place
For Lumberjane scouts
And for everyone else.

Now, I'm not gonna lie to you girls, you're gonna See some stuff this summer. Stuff you might not understand. It'll be hard. But you're scouts, and you're made of tougher stuff. So remember that pledge you took, and stick together no matter what. You hear me?

Stop by my table at breakfast so I can give you your Up All Night badges.

Sooo, that's a "no" on the parents thing, or...?

will co...

The...
It hel...
appearan...
dress f...
Further...
Lumber...
to have...
part in...
Thiskv...
Hardc...
have...
them...

...E UNIFORM

...should be worn at camp
...events when Lumberjanes
...n may also be worn at other
...ions. It should be worn as a
...the uniform dress with
...rect shoes, and stocking or
...out grows her uniform or
...ng...ter Lumberjane.
...a she has
...n her
...f her

LITTLE RED FORMATION!

ROANOKE CABIN

The...
yellow, short sl...
emb...
the w...
choose...
slacks,...
made o...
out-of-do...
green bere...
the colla...
Shoes ma...
heels, rou...ngs or
socks shou... n the shoes or wi...
the uniform. Ne...es, bracelets, or other jewelry do...
belong with a Lumberjane uniform.

...CES

CAMP

HOW TO WEAR THE UNIFORM

To look well in a uniform demans first of...
uniform be kept in good condition—clean...
pressed. See that the skirt is the right length for you...
height and build, that the belt is adjusted to your w...
that your shoes and stockings are in keeping with t...
uniform, that you watch your posture and carry yourself...
with dignity and grace. If the beret is removed indoors,
be sure that your hair is neat and kept in place with an
insconspicuous clip or ribbon. When you wear a
Lumberjane uniform you are identified as a member of
this organization and you should be doubly careful to
conduct yourself in a way that will show everyone that
courtesy and thoughtfullness are part of being a
Lumberjane. People are likely to judge a whole nation by
the selfishness of a few individuals, to criticize a whole
family because of the misconduct of one member, and to
feel unkindly toward and organization because of the

helps to cre...
in a group. I...
active life th...
another bond...
future, and pr...
in order to b...
Lumberjane pr...
Penniquiqul Thi... ...ore Lady
Types, but m... ...es will wish to have one. They
can either bu...s, or make it themselves from
materials available at the trading post.

JENNY,
OUR CABIN LEADER!

LUMBERJANES FIELD MANUAL

CHAPTER TWO

Lumberjanes "Sports and Games" Program Field

NAVAL GAUGING BADGE

"Because drowning is a scary way to go."

Lumberjanes are considered to be girls who can find their way around any situation, whether it be an unsuspecting adventure in the great outdoors to the problem solving of every day matters. As a modern Lumberjane, you will be able to recognize the importance of naval abilities and how to navigate any stream. A Lumberjane will be able to find her way through any rapid, fall, or even quiet wilderness. Will understand the importance of safety and always be wary of the false sense of security that the wilderness can lull any unsuspecting person into, a Lumberjane will remain ready and able to adapt to whatever is thrown at her.

The *Naval Gauging* badge is a sense of pride for any Lumberjane, as she continues her journey through the daily trials that every Lumberjane must face. Not only will a Lumberjane learn how to forage in the wild, learn how to care for herself and her friends on the trail, be she will learn how to explore with a seeing and vigilant eye. She will make herself at home in the woods, and any future place she finds fitting for herself.

To obtain the *Naval Gauging* badge a Lumberjane must be able to tie rapidly six different knots. She will find herself well versed in rope work as it can be extremely important in her future adventure, she must know how to splice ropes, use a palm and needle, and fling a rope coil. A Lumberjane must be able to row, pole, scull, and steer a boat; also bring a boat properly alongside and make fast. She must know how to box the compass, read a chart, and show use of parallel rules and dividers. She must be able to state direction by the stars and sun, and be capable of swimming fifty yards with shoes and clothes on. She will know the importances of a life preserver, CPR, and the basic understanding of how to respond in emergency situations. She must understand

-THUNK!-

will co

The
It help
appearan
dress f
Further
Lumber
to have
part in
Thiskv
Hardc
have
them

The
yellow, short sl
emb
the w
choose
slacks,
made o
out-of-do
green bere
the colla
Shoes ma
heels, rou   ings on
socks shou   with the shoes or wi
the uniform. Ne   es, bracelets, or other jewelry do
belong with a Lumberjane uniform.

HOW TO WEAR THE UNIFORM

To look well in a uniform demans first of
uniform be kept in good condition—clean
pressed. See that the skirt is the right length f
height and build, that the belt is adjusted to
that your shoes and stockings are in keeping
uniform, that you watch your posture and carry
with dignity and grace. If the beret is removed i
be sure that your hair is neat and kept in place wit
insconspicuous clip or ribbon. When you wear
Lumberjane uniform you are identified as a member
this organization and you should be doubly careful to
conduct yourself in a way that will show everyone that
courtesy and thoughtfullness are part of being a
Lumberjane. People are likely to judge a whole nation by
the selfishness of a few individuals, to criticize a whole
family because of the misconduct of one member, and to
feel unkindly toward and organization because of the

out grows her uniform or
ter Lumberjane.
a she has
her
her

e life th
another bond
future, and pr
in order to b
Lumberjane pr
Penniquiqul Thi   ore Lady
Types, but m   s will wish to have one. They
can either b   e, or make it themselves from
materials available at the trading post.

LUMBERJANES FIELD MANUAL

CHAPTER THREE

Lumberjanes "Mathematics and Science" Program Field

EVERYTHING UNDER THE SUM BADGE

"Math leads to a basic understanding of life."

While math is an important subject in schooling, a Lumberjane will learn the commonplace use in everyday situations from knowing the proper amount of kindling needed for a variety of fires to know the velocity needed to run in order to leap across a cliff and make it to the other side. A Lumberjane recognizes how basic understanding of equations can not only make the trials of the wilderness simpler but how furthering that knowledge will help them establish a firmer foothold in the adventure of their lifetime. The human experience can be boiled down to patterns and it is with this understanding that a Lumberjane sees her importance not only in the lives that she directly influences but those outside her circle.

To obtain the *Everything Under the Sum* badge, a Lumberjane must be able to map accurately and correctly from the country itself the main features of half a mile of road, with 440 yards each side to a scale of two feet to

the mile, and afterward draw same map from memory. A Lumberjane must be able to measure the height of a tree, telegraph pole, and church steeple, describing method adopted. She must be able to measure the width of a river, estimate distance apart of two objects a known distance away and unapproachable. With this skill she will be able fully prepare for her adventure or task, but be able to set her friends up for success as they go on their journey together.

With an *Everything Under the Sum* badge, a Lumberjane will be able to measure a gradient, have a basic understand of theoretical mathematics and the basic of laws of physics, this will help give her a sure footing in her future career whether it be teaching the future generations or answering their patriotic call and going into the service of their country. While this badge may take some time to earn, every Lumberjane will be able to understand it's importance and, while working

will co...

The...
It hel...
appearan...
dress fo...
Further...
Lumber...
to have...
part in...
Thisky...
Hardo...
have...
them...

The...
yellow, short sl...
emb...
the w...
choose...
slacks,...
made o...
out-of-do...
green bere...
the colla...
Shoes ma...
heels, rou...
socks shou...
the uniform. Ne... ...es, bracelets, or other jewelry do ...
belong with a Lumberjane uniform.

HOW TO WEAR THE UNIF...

To look well in a uniform deman...
uniform be kept in good con...
pressed. See that the skirt is the rig...
height and build, that the belt is adju...
that your shoes and stockings are in ke...
uniform, that you watch your posture and ca...
with dignity and grace. If the beret is removed i...
be sure that your hair is neat and kept in place with...
insonspicuous clip or ribbon. When you wear a
Lumberjane uniform you are identified as a member of
this organization and you should be doubly careful to
conduct yourself in a way that will show everyone that
courtesy and thoughtfullness are part of being a
Lumberjane. People are likely to judge a whole nation by
the selfishness of a few individuals, to criticize a whole
family because of the misconduct of one member, and to
feel unkindly toward and organization because of the

...E UNIFORM

...should be worn at camp
...events when Lumberjanes
...n may also be worn at other
...ions. It should be worn as a
...the uniform dress with
...rrect shoes, and stocking or
...out grows her uniform or
...ng ...ter Lumberjane.
...a she has
...n her
...f her

The unifor...
helps to cre...
in a group. ...
active life th...
another bond...
future, and pr...
in order to b...
Lumberjane pr...
Penniquiqul Thi... ...re Lady
Types, but m... ...es will wish to have one. They
can either bu... ...or make it themselves from
materials available at the trading post.

LUMBERJANES FIELD MANUAL

CHAPTER FOUR

Lumberjanes "Sports and Games" Program Field

ROBYN HOOD BADGE

"A sharp eye shows sharp wit."

Hand and eye coordination is not only important for day-to-day activities, but can be instrumental in a Lumberjane's experience with nature. In these modern times the basic practices of what was once a right practice is seen more as a sport, but the Lumberjanes recognize the importance of not only the respect and care of their tools, but by training with their fellow Lumberjanes, they will learn to trust in not only each other, but in themselves and the skills the they already possess. It is important for a Lumberjane to know that she can rely upon herself in the great vastness of nature and that she will not be reliant on the machine manufactured tools of modern day but that with her own two hands she will be able to step forward into whatever life throws at her.

The skill of archery teaches every Lumberjane the importance of a good posture, the finesse needed when handling delicate instruments, the necessary upper arm strength and the poise of being able to take down prey from a great distance. Before a Lumberjane can earn her *Robyn Hood* badge, it is important for her to learn within the safety of the camp's archery range. She will be given the tools that she needs to succeed and with the support of her friends she will be able to hone her ability and gain the confidence she needs to send the arrow to it's target.

To obtain the *Robyn Hood* badge, a Lumberjane must first make a bow and arrow which will shoot a distance of one hundred feet with fair precision. It is an essential task that will let her learn about the benefits of putting time into a job to do it right. She must prove her knowledge of basic archery safety both in the range and outside. She must make a total score of 350 with 60 shots in one or two meets, using standard four-foot target at forty yards or three-foot target at thirty yards. She must be able to make a total score of 300 with 72 arrows, using standard

will co

The

It hel
appearan
dress fo
Further
Lumber
to have
part in
Thiskv
Hardo
have
them

The
yellow, short sl
emb
the w
choose
slacks,
made o
out-of-do
green bere
the colla
Shoes ma
heels, rou
socks shou
the uniform. Ne   es, bracelets, or other jewelry do
belong with a Lumberjane uniform.

UNIFORM

hould be worn at camp
events when Lumberjanes
n may also be worn at other
ions. It should be worn as a
the uniform dress with
rect shoes, and stocking or
out grows her uniform or
ter Lumberjane.
a she has
her
her

ES

WHY ARE HIPSTER YETIS SO ODD? BECAUSE THEY CAN'T EVEN.

FRIENDSHIP TO THE MAX!

SERIOUSLY?

HOW TO WEAR THE UNIFORM

To look well in a uniform demans first of
uniform be kept in good condition—clean
pressed. See that the skirt is the right length for your own
height and build, that the belt is adjusted to your waist
that your shoes and stockings are in keeping with
uniform, that you watch your posture and carry
with dignity and grace. If the beret is remov
be sure that your hair is neat and kept in pl
insconspicuous clip or ribbon. When you
Lumberjane uniform you are identified as a memb
this organization and you should be doubly careful
conduct yourself in a way that will show everyone that
courtesy and thoughtfullness are part of being a
Lumberjane. People are likely to judge a whole nation by
the selfishness of a few individuals, to criticize a whole
family because of the misconduct of one member, and to
feel unkindly toward and organization because of the

pri
to b
mberjane pr
enniquiqul Thi   ore Lady
Types, but m   es will wish to have one. They
can either bu   ns, or make it themselves from
materials available at the trading post.

COVER GALLERY

Lumberjanes "Out-of-Doors" Program Field

PUNGEON MASTER BADGE

"The best kind of punishment."

The pun conundrum is that most view it as the lowest form of word-play, but we Lumberjanes say, if it was good enough for Shakespeare and Plautus, then it is definitely good enough of our camp literary masters. The original purpose of a pun seems to be as diverse as the circumstances in how they first appeared in modern culture, and can be seen as more than a mere linguistic fillip. Lumberjanes recognize the value of a good pun and its cleverly worded effect on those around us and the future of civilization. A Lumberjane not only enjoys the creativity behind a pun but the importance of how it can bring a group together.

Wordplay is a great technique that Lumberjanes will continue to pursue with the fervor of every other skill they will learn at camp, and while this badge is the most popular, a Lumberjane knows the importances of not rushing head first into this lesson. A pun is meant for a perfect moment in time and the *Pungeon Master* badge teaches all Lumberjanes the importance of not only playing close attention to their current situation and their surroundings, but how to stay on their toes with their wit so always be available to improve the conversation around them.

To obtain the *Pungeon Master* badge, a Lumberjane must have a knowledge of the game laws of the state in which she lives. Great care must be taken to determine if it is the appropriate time or place for clever wordplay as a Lumberjane may also risk her pun being misconstrued. It is important to find not only the the right audience, but time and place in order to ensure that a pun will not be missed. She must preserve the importance of the pun and truly understand the strength of the words she is using. A Lumberjane understands the importance of a pun and the power that comes with it.

Issue One
NOELLE STEVENSON

Issue One Variant
LAUREN ZUKE

Issue Four Variant
KRIS ANKA